LITERATURE & WRITING WORKSHOP

EXPLORING
PLAYS

SCHOLASTIC INC.

PERMISSIONS— "Strong Wind and Rough Face Girl" by Adam Grant from SCHOLASTIC STORYWORKS, November-December 1993. Copyright © 1993 by Scholastic Inc. Used by permission. "The Book that Saved the Earth" Reprinted by permission from PLAYS AND PROGRAMS FOR BOYS AND GIRLS, by Claire Boiko. Copyright © 1972 by Claire Boiko. Publishers: Plays, Inc., Boston, MA. Dramatization of Sir Arthur Conan Doyle's "The Bascombe Valley Mystery" published in SCHOLASTIC SCOPE, November 2, 1984. Copyright © 1984 by Scholastic Inc. Used by permission.

ISBN 0-590-49540-2

Copyright © 1994 by Scholastic Inc. All rights reserved. Published by Scholastic Inc. Materials in unit may be used for classroom use by purchaser. All other permissions must be obtained from the publisher.

CONTENTS

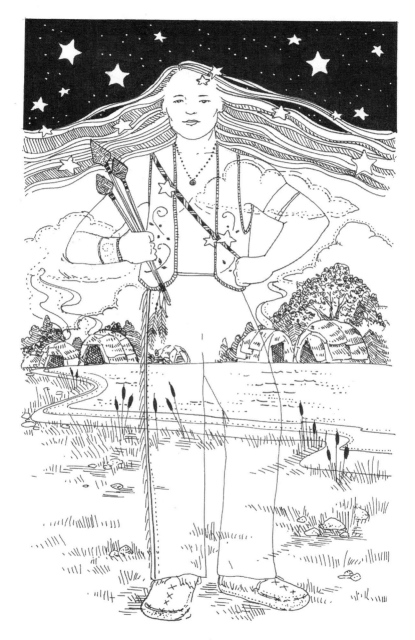

Strong Wind and Rough Face Girl

by
Adam Grant

Illustrated by
Janice Fried

CHARACTERS:

Narrator 1
Narrator 2
Strong Wind (a great warrior)
Clear Sky (his sister)
Chief
Rough Face Girl
Fallen Leaf   } (chief's daughters)
Crooked Branch

Agreat and powerful warrior needs a wife. *Three sisters hope to marry him, but only one who is good and honest can succeed. This play is based on a Native American story from the Algonquin Nation. It is hundreds of years old, but it may remind you of a tale you have heard before.*

Narrator 1
Long ago in a lakeside village, Strong Wind lived with his sister, Clear Sky. He had a magical gift. He could make himself invisible.

Narrator 2
This gift made him a great and legendary warrior. He was the most respected man in the village, as well loved as the Chief. But there was something missing in his life.

Clear Sky
Strong Wind, you look sad. You haven't slept lately. Are you ill? Has the hunt not been successful?

Strong Wind
No, I am as strong as ever, and the spirits have provided us with great bounty this season. Yet there is an empty space in my heart. I feel sad and incomplete.

Clear Sky
I know what is troubling you. You are lonely. We must find you a wife.

Narrator 1
Strong Wind frowned. He had not thought of this before. A great warrior must have a wife and children, or else his life is only filled with battles.

Clear Sky
Don't look sad. There are plenty of beautiful women in the village.

Strong Wind
But my bride must have a beautiful spirit and perfect honesty. That is even more important than her appearance. She will not be easy to find.

Clear Sky
We must devise a test to find one who is right for you.

Narrator 2
Strong Wind and Clear Sky talked far into the night and came up with a plan. Clear Sky would bring women from the village to meet Strong Wind. He would make himself invisible. If any woman could still see him, he would know that she was special and was the right woman for him.

Strong Wind
This is a good plan. I will sleep well tonight.

Narrator 1
News of Strong Wind's search for a wife spread quickly in the village. Even the Chief's tent was buzzing, for he had three young daughters.

SCENE 2

Narrator 2
The youngest of the daughters was smart, happy, honest, and beautiful. But after her mother's death, the girl became sad and quiet. She had been a favorite of everyone in the village, including her father. This made her two older sisters jealous.

Narrator 1
After their mother died, the older sisters were terribly cruel to the youngest. They cut all her hair off and tore her clothes. They always made her tend the fire. Sparks flew out and burned her face and hands. Now, everyone called her Rough Face Girl.

Fallen Leaf
Rough Face Girl! Get me my new moccasins. I'm going to win Strong Wind's hand.

Crooked Branch
Rough Face Girl, bring me my bead necklace, and hurry up. I'm going too. He'll surely pick one of us.

Rough Face Girl
Maybe I should go too.

Fallen Leaf
What? You? Look at yourself. Strong Wind would marry a mole before he would even look at you.

Crooked Branch
You might be father's favorite, but no one will marry you when there are girls like us around. Now go to work. Don't let that cooking fire die out!

SCENE 3

Narrator 2
That night, Clear Sky brought Fallen Leaf and Crooked Branch to Strong Wind's tent.

Crooked Branch
You might as well send Fallen Leaf away. I know I will win. Besides, I'm much prettier than her and have a much better personality.

Narrator 1
Strong Wind walked in front of them. He was invisible and made no noise.

Clear Sky
Do you see him?

Crooked Branch
Oh, yes!

Clear Sky
Then tell me, with what does he pull his sled?

Narrator 2
Crooked Branch tried to quickly make something up.

Crooked Branch
Oh, he pulls it with rawhide!

Narrator 1
Knowing that Crooked Branch was lying, Strong Wind spoke.

Strong Wind

She lies. Send her away!

Narrator 2

Next, Fallen Leaf tried her luck, but with much the same result.

SCENE 4

Narrator 1

Being found out as liars, the two sisters soon were home in the Chief's tent, angry and embarrassed. Rough Face Girl and the Chief were waiting for them.

Chief

Well, which one of you will marry Strong Wind?

Fallen Leaf

Neither one of us, Father. We failed.

Rough Face Girl

Oh Father, perhaps I should try to win him. Wouldn't you be happy for me if I did?

Fallen Leaf

You? Ha ha ha. With that face? Don't be ridiculous!

Chief

Stop that! You are cruel for no reason. Go outside. I want to talk to Rough Face Girl alone.

Narrator 1

When Fallen Leaf and Crooked Branch had gone, the Chief looked at his young daughter. He loved her and didn't want her feelings hurt. Finally, he spoke.

Chief

Rough Face Girl, if you want to try to win Strong Wind then go ahead. Don't let anyone talk you out of following your heart. Maybe Strong Wind will see the beautiful soul and honest spirit that your mother saw and that I still see every time I look at you.

Narrator 2

Rough Face Girl threw her arms around her father and smiled.

SCENE 5

Narrator 1

At dusk, Rough Face Girl met Clear Sky outside Strong Wind's tent.

Rough Face Girl

Clear Sky, I am ready.

Clear Sky

Rough Face Girl, can you see Strong Wind?

Rough Face Girl

No, I cannot.

Narrator 2

Clear Sky was surprised. No one had ever answered the question truthfully before.

Clear Sky

Try harder. Do you see him now?

Narrator 1

All of a sudden, a magnificent man came into Rough Face Girl's view.

Rough Face Girl
Oh, yes. I see him, and he is wonderful!

Clear Sky
With what does he pull his sled?

Rough Face Girl
With a rainbow.

Narrator 2
Clear Sky gasped. She knew this answer was also true.

Clear Sky
What does he use for a bowstring?

Narrator 1
Rough Face Girl could see Strong Wind perfectly now. He was smiling.

Rough Face Girl
He uses the Milky Way.

Narrator 2
Strong Wind came into view of both women and took Rough Face Girl's hand in his.

Strong Wind
This is the woman I have searched for. She was the only one who spoke the truth from the beginning. And she is beautiful too.

Narrator 1
Then Clear Sky knew that Strong Wind had fallen in love when Rough Face Girl answered the first question truthfully. That was why he made himself visible.

Clear Sky
Welcome, Rough Face Girl. Welcome into our family.

Narrator 2

Strong Wind and Rough Face Girl were married the next day and lived a long and happy life. In time, the love they shared swept away the scars on Rough Face Girl's skin, and her hair grew long and black, until she could no longer remember her unhappy life with her sisters.

Narrator 1

As punishment for lying to him, Strong Wind turned Fallen Leaf and Crooked Branch into open trees and planted them in the earth. Even today, the leaves of aspen trees shiver in fear whenever Strong Wind passes them, no matter how softly.

The Book That Saved The Earth

Illustrated by
Doug Krunston

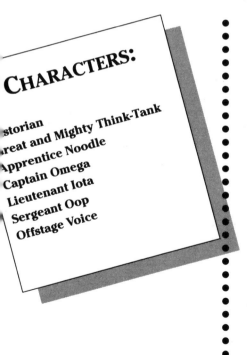

CHARACTERS:

Historian
Great and Mighty Think-Tank
Apprentice Noodle
Captain Omega
Lieutenant Iota
Sergeant Oop
Offstage Voice

SCENE 1

Before Rise: Spotlight shines on Historian, who is sitting at a table down right, on which there is a movie projector. A sign on an easel beside him reads: Museum of Ancient History: Department of the Twentieth Century. He stands and bows to audience.

Historian
    Good afternoon. Welcome to our Museum of Ancient History, and to

17

my department—curiosities of the good old, far-off twentieth century. The twentieth century was often called the Era of the Book. In those days, there were books about everything from anteaters to Zulus. Books taught people how to, and when to, and where to, and why to. They illustrated, educated, punctuated and even decorated. But the strangest thing a book ever did was to save the Earth. You haven't heard about the Martian invasion of 1980? Tsk, tsk. What *do* they teach children nowadays? Well, you know, the invasion never really happened, because a single book stopped it. What was that book, you ask? A noble encyclopedia? A tome about rockets and missiles? A secret file from outer space? No, it was none of these. It was—but here, let me turn on the historiscope and show you what happened many, many centuries ago, in 1980. *(He turns on the projector and points it left. Spotlight on* Historian *goes out, and comes up down left on* Think-Tank, *who is seated on a raised box, arms folded. He has a huge, egg-shaped head, and he wears a long robe decorated with stars and circles.* Apprentice Noodle *stands beside him at an elaborate switchboard. A sign on an easel reads:* Mars Space Control. Great and Mighty Think-Tank: Commander-In-Chief. Bow Low Before Entering.)

Noodle
(Bowing) 0 Great and Mighty Think-Tank, most powerful and intelligent creature in the whole universe, what are your orders?

Think-Tank
(Peevishly) You left out part of my salutation, Apprentice Noodle. Go over the whole thing again.

Noodle

It shall be done, sir. *(In singsong)* 0 Great and Mighty Think-Tank, Ruler of Mars and her two moons, most powerful and intelligent creature in the whole universe— *(Out of breath)* What-are-your-orders?

Think-Tank

That's better, Noodle. I wish to be placed in communication with our manned space probe to that ridiculous little planet we are going to put under our generous rulership. What do they call it again?

Noodle

Earth, Your Intelligence.

Think-Tank

Earth—of course. You see how insignificant the place is? But first, something important. My mirror. I wish to consult my mirror.

Noodle

It shall be done, sir. *(He hands* Think-Tank *a hand mirror.)*

Think-Tank

Mirror, mirror, in my hand, who is the most fantastically intellectually gifted being in the land?

Offstage Voice

(After a pause) You, sir.

Think-Tank

(Striking mirror) Quicker. Answer quicker next time. I hate a slow mirror. *(He admires himself.)* Ah, there I am. Are we Martians not a handsome race? So much more attractive than those ugly earthlings with their tiny heads.

Noodle, you keep on exercising your mind, and someday you'll have a balloon brain just like mine.

Noodle
Oh, I hope so, Mighty Think-Tank. I hope so.

Think-Tank
Now, contact the space probe. I want to invade that primitive ball of mud called Earth before lunch.

Noodle
It shall be done, sir. *(He twists knobs and adjusts levers on switchboard. Electronic buzzes and beeps are heard.* Noodle *and* Think-Tank *remain at controls as curtains open.)*

Setting: *The Centerville Public Library.*

At Rise: Captain Omega *stands at center, opening and closing card catalogue drawers, looking puzzled.* Lieutenant Iota *is up left, counting books in bookcase.* Sergeant Oop *is at right, opening and closing a book, turning it upside down, shaking it, and then rifling pages and shaking his head.*

Noodle
(Adjusting knobs) I have a close sighting of the space crew, sir. (Think-Tank *puts on pair of huge goggles and turns toward stage to watch.)* They seem to have entered some sort of Earth structure.

Think Tank
Excellent. Make voice contact.

Noodle
(Speaking into a microphone) Mars Space Control calling the crew of Probe One. Mars Space Control calling the

crew of Probe One. Come in, Captain Omega. Give us your location.

Captain Omega
(Speaking into a disc, which is on a chain around his neck) Captain Omega to Mars Space Control. Lieutenant Iota, Sergeant Oop and I have landed on Earth without incident. We have taken shelter in this *(Indicates room)*— this square place. Have you any idea where we are, Lieutenant Iota?

Iota
I can't figure it out, Captain. *(Holding up book)* I've counted two thousand of these peculiar things. This place must be some sort of storage barn. What do you think, Sergeant Oop?

Oop
I haven't a clue. I've been to seven galaxies, but I've never seen anything like this. Maybe they're hats. *(He opens book and puts it on his head.)* Say, maybe this is a haberdasher's store!

Omega
(Bowing low) Perhaps the Great and Mighty Think-Tank will give us the benefit of his thought on the matter.

Think-Tank
Elementary, my dear Omega. Hold one of the items up so that I may view it closely *(Omega holds book on the palm of his hand.)* Yes, yes, I understand now. Since Earth creatures are always eating, the place in which you find yourselves is undoubtedly a crude refreshment stand.

Omega
(To Iota and Oop) He says we're in a refreshment stand.

Oop

Well, the Earthlings certainly have a strange diet.

Think-Tank

That item in your hand is called a "sandwich."

Omega

(Nodding) A sandwich.

Iota

(Nodding) A sandwich.

Oop

(Taking book from his head) A sandwich?

Think-Tank

Sandwiches are the main staple of Earth diet. Look at it closely. *(Omega squints at book.)* There are two slices of what is called "bread," and between them there is some sort of filling.

Omega

That is correct, sir.

Think-Tank

To confirm my opinion, I order you to eat it.

Omega

(Gulping) Eat it?

Think-Tank

Do you doubt the Mighty Think-Tank?

Omega

Oh, no, no. But poor Lieutenant Iota has not had his breakfast. Lieutenant Iota, I order you to eat this—this sandwich.

Iota

(*Dubiously*) Eat it? Oh, Captain! It's a very great honor to be the first Martian to eat a sandwich, I'm sure, but-but how can I be so impolite as to eat before my Sergeant? (*Handing* Oop *book; brightly*) Sergeant Oop, I order you to eat the sandwich.

Oop

(*Making a face*) Who, sir? Me, sir?

Iota *and* Omega

(*Slapping their chests in a salute*) For the glory of Mars, Oop!

Oop

Yes, sirs. (*Unhappily*) Immediately, sirs. (*He opens his mouth wide. Omega and* Iota *watch him breathlessly. He bites down on a corner of the book and pantomimes chewing and swallowing, while making terrible faces.*)

Omega

Well, Oop?

Iota

Well, Oop? (*Oop coughs. Omega and Iota pound him on back.*)

Think-Tank

Was it not delicious, Sergeant Oop?

Oop

(*Slapping his chest in salute*) That is correct, sir. It was *not* delicious. I don't know how the Earthlings can get those sandwiches down without water. They're dry as Martian dust.

Noodle

Sir—O Great and Mighty Think-Tank. I beg your pardon, but an insignificant bit of data floated into my mind about those sandwiches.

Think-Tank

It can't be worth much, but go ahead. Give us your trifling bit of data.

Noodle

Well, sir, I have seen surveyor films of those sandwiches. I noticed that the Earthlings did not eat them. They used them as some sort of communication device.

Think-Tank

(Haughtily) Naturally. That was my next point. These are actually communication sandwiches. Think-Tank is never wrong. Who is never wrong?

All

(Saluting) Great and Mighty Think-Tank is never wrong.

Think-Tank

Therefore, I order you to listen to them.

Omega

Listen to them?

Iota *and* Oop

(To each other; puzzled) Listen to them?

Think-Tank

Do you have marbles in your ears? I said, listen to them. *(Martians bow very low.)*

Omega

It shall be done, sir. *(They each take two books from a bookcase, and hold them to their ears, listening intently.)*

25

Iota
(*Whispering to* Omega) Do you hear anything?

Omega
(*Whispering back*) Nothing. Do you hear anything, Oop?

Oop
(*Loudly*) Not a thing! (*Omega* and *Iota* jump in fright.)

Think-Tank
Well? Well? Report to me. What do you hear?

Omega
Nothing, sir. Perhaps we are not on the correct frequency.

Iota
Nothing, sir. Perhaps the Earthlings have sharper ears than we do.

Oop
I don't hear a thing. Maybe these sandwiches don't make sounds.

Think-Tank
What? What? Does someone suggest the Mighty Think-Tank has made a mistake?

Omega
Oh, no, sir. No, sir. We'll keep listening.

Noodle
Please excuse me, Your Brilliance, but a cloudy piece of information is rolling around in my head.

Think-Tank
Well, roll it out, Noodle, and I will clarify it for you.

Noodle
I seem to recall that the Earthlings did not *listen* to the sandwiches. They opened them, and watched them.

Think-Tank
Yes, that is quite correct. I will clarify that for you, Captain Omega. Those sandwiches are not for ear communication, they are for eye communication. Now,

Captain Omega, take that large, bright-colored sandwich over there. It appears to be important. Tell me what you observe. *(Omega picks up a very large copy of "Mother Goose," holding it so that the audience can see the title.* Iota *looks over* Omega's *left shoulder, and* Oop *squints over his right shoulder.)*

Omega

It appears to contain pictures of Earthlings.

Iota

There seems to be some sort of code.

Think-Tank

(Sharply interested) Code? Code? I told you this was important. Describe the code.

Oop

It's little lines and squiggles and dots. Thousands of them, next to the pictures.

Think-Tank

Code. Perhaps the Earthlings are not so primitive as we have thought. We must break the code. We must.

Noodle

Forgive me, Your Cleverness, but did not the chemical department give our spacemen a supply of Vitamin X to increase their intelligence?

Think-Tank

Stop! A thought of magnificent brilliance has come to me. Spacemen, our chemical department has given you a supply of Vitamin X to increase your intelligence. Take it immediately and then watch the sandwich. The meaning of the code will slowly unfold before you.

Omega

It shall be done, sir. Remove pill. *(Crew takes vitamins from boxes on their belts.)* Present Vitamin X. *(They hold vitamins out in front of them, stiffly.)* Swallow. *(They put vitamins into their mouths and gulp simultaneously. They open their eyes wide, shake their heads, and they put their hands to their foreheads.)* The cotangent of a given angle in a right triangle is equal to the adjacent side divided by the hypotenuse.

Iota

Habeas corpus ad faciendum et recipiendum!

Oop

There is change of pressure along a radius in curvilinear motion.

Think-Tank

Excellent. Now, decipher that code.

All

It shall be done, sir. *(They frown over book, turning pages.)*

Omega

(Brightly) Aha!

Iota

(Brightly) Oho!

Oop

(Bursting into laughter) Ha, ha, ha!

Think-Tank

What does it say? Tell me this instant. Transcribe, Omega.

Omega

Yes, sir. *(He reads with great seriousness.)*
"Mistress Mary, quite contrary,
How does your garden grow'?
With cockle shells and silver bells
And pretty maids all in a row."

Oop

Ha, ha, ha. Imagine that. Pretty maids growing in a
garden.

Think-Tank

(Alarmed) Stop! This is no time for levity. Don't you realize the seriousness of this discovery? The Earthlings have discovered how to combine agriculture and mining. They can actually grow crops of rare metals such as silver. And cockle shells. They can grow high explosives, too. Noodle, contact our invasion fleet.

Noodle

They are ready to go down and take over Earth, sir.

Think-Tank

Tell them to hold. Tell them new information has come to us about Earth. Iota, continue transcribing.

Iota

Yes, sir. *(He reads very gravely.)*
"Hey diddle diddle! The cat and the fiddle,
The cow jumped over the moon,
The little dog laughed to see such sport,
And the dish ran away with the spoon."

Oop

(Laughing) The dish ran away with the spoon!

Think-Tank

Cease laughter. Desist. This is more and more alarming. The Earthlings have reached a high level of civilization. Didn't you hear? They have taught their domesticated animals musical culture and space techniques. Even their dogs have a sense of humor. Why at this very moment, they may be launching an interplanetary attack of millions of *cows!* Notify the invasion fleet. No invasion today. Oop, transcribe the next code.

Oop

Yes, sir. *(Reading)*
"Humpty Dumpty sat on the wall,
Humpty Dumpty had a great fall;
All the King's horses and all the King's men,
Couldn't put Humpty Dumpty together again."
Oh, look, sir. Here's a picture of Humpty Dumpty. Why,
sir, he looks like—he looks like—*(Turns large picture of
Humpty Dumpty toward* Think-Tank *and audience.)*

Think-Tank

(Screaming and holding his head) It's me! It's my Great
and Mighty Balloon Brain. The Earthlings have seen me.
They're after me. "Had a great fall!" That means they plan
to capture Mars Central Control and me! It's an invasion
of Mars! Noodle, prepare a space capsule for me. I must
escape without delay. Spacemen, you must leave Earth
at once, but be sure to remove all traces of your visit. The
Earthlings must not know that I know—*(Omega, Iota and*
Oop *rush about, putting books back on shelves.)*

Noodle

Where shall we go, sir?

Think-Tank

A hundred million miles away from Mars. Order the
invasion fleet to evacuate the entire planet of Mars. We
are heading for Alpha Centauri, a hundred million miles
away. *(Omega, Iota, and* Oop *run off right, as* Noodle *helps*
Think-Tank *off left and curtain closes. Spotlight shines on*
Historian *down right.)*

Historian

(Chuckling) And that's how one dusty old book of
nursery rhymes saved the world from a Martian invasion.

As you all know, in the twenty-fifth century, five hundred years after all this happened, we Earthlings resumed contact with Mars, and we even became very chummy with the Martians. By that time, Great and Mighty Think-Tank had been replaced by a very clever Martian—the Wise and Wonderful Noodle! Oh, yes, we taught the Martians the difference between sandwiches and books. We taught them how to read, too, and we established a model library in their capital city of Marsopolis. But, as you might expect, there is still one book that the Martians can never bring themselves to read. You've guessed it— *Mother Goose! (He bows and exits right.)*

The Boscombe Valley Mystery

a dramatization of a Sherlock Holmes mystery by
Sir Arthur Conan Doyle

Illustrated by
Eva Vagretti Cockrille

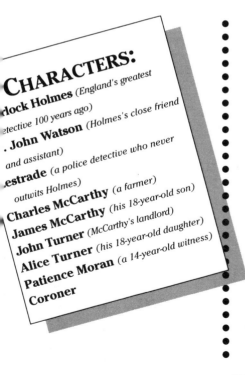

CHARACTERS:

...lock Holmes *(England's greatest ...tective 100 years ago)*

. John Watson *(Holmes's close friend and assistant)*

...estrade *(a police detective who never outwits Holmes)*

Charles McCarthy *(a farmer)*

James McCarthy *(his 18-year-old son)*

John Turner *(McCarthy's landlord)*

Alice Turner *(his 18-year-old daughter)*

Patience Moran *(a 14-year-old witness)*

Coroner

SCENE 1

Holmes and Watson are in a train going from London to Boscombe Valley to investigate a mystery. Holmes is silent at first, reading newspaper accounts of the case.

Holmes
(Turning to Watson) Thank you for meeting me on such short notice, Watson. When I asked you to join me, I knew little about the case. Have you heard anything about it?

35

Watson
Not a word. I haven't read a newspaper for several days.

Holmes
The newspapers don't really tell very much. It seems to be one of those simple cases that is actually difficult. The police have built a strong case against the son of the murdered man.

Watson
So it's murder.

Holmes
It appears to be. Last Monday afternoon, Charles McCarthy left his house to walk to Boscombe Pool. He told his housekeeper that he had an appointment there at 3:00. He did not come back from that appointment alive.

Watson
Did anyone see him after he left his house?

Holmes
Yes. McCarthy's landlord, John Turner, owns a hunting lodge near Boscombe Pool. The lodgekeeper's wife saw McCarthy walk by. She said he was alone. Then she saw McCarthy's son, James, going the same way a few minutes later. James carried a rifle. Not long after that, the lodgekeeper's daughter saw James and his father beside Boscombe Pool...

SCENE 2

The lodge near Boscombe Pool on the day of the murder. Patience Moran, who is 14 years old, runs inside to her mother.

Patience

(Frightened) Mother! I just saw Mr. McCarthy and his son having a terrible quarrel. Mr. McCarthy was shouting. Suddenly James raised his hand, as if to hit his father. I was so afraid that they were going to fight that I came home. Do you think they will hurt each other?

(Just then, James McCarthy runs into the lodge. His right hand and sleeve are stained with blood.)

James

(Very upset) My father is dead! I found him beside the pool! Can someone help me carry him home?

SCENE 3

Back to Holmes and Watson on the train.

Holmes

Charles McCarthy was hit over the head with something heavy. The police think the weapon was the butt of James's rifle. It was found lying near the body, and James was arrested. Those are the main facts of the case.

Watson

It certainly looks as if James is guilty. All the facts point to him as the murderer.

Holmes

Detective Lestrade is working on the case. He is sure that James McCarthy is guilty. But there are several people in the neighborhood who believe he is innocent. Among them is Alice Turner, the daughter of the McCarthy's landlord. She is the one who called me in on the case.

Watson

(Shaking his head) I am afraid that the facts are so obvious that James cannot be innocent.

Holmes

(Smiling) There is nothing more misleading than an obvious fact. I believe we will find some facts which are not so obvious to Detective Lestrade.

Watson

(Puzzled) What do you mean?

Holmes

You might be interested in reading James McCarthy's statement to the coroner. They are in this newspaper article. *(He hands one of the newspapers to Watson.)*

SCENE 4

The coroner's office the day after the murder. The coroner is questioning James McCarthy.

Coroner

Why did you follow your father to Boscombe Pool?

James

I didn't know I was following him. I had been away from home for three days. When I got back, I decided to go rabbit hunting. I took my rifle and headed for Boscombe Pool. When I was almost there, I heard a cry of "Cooee!" That was a signal between my father and me. I went forward to meet him, but he seemed surprised to see me.

Coroner

What happened then?

James

We had a talk, which led to a quarrel. I left when my father lost his temper.

Coroner

What made you go back to his side?

James

I heard him cry out. I ran back and found him lying on the ground. His head was bleeding. I dropped my rifle and held him in my arms. He died almost instantly. Since Mr. Turner's hunting lodge was nearby, I ran there for help.

Coroner

Did your father say anything to you just before he died?

James

He mumbled something about a rat.

Coroner

Did you know what he meant by that?

James

No.

Coroner

What had you and your father been quarreling about?

James

I would rather not say. It had nothing to do with the tragedy that followed.

Coroner

If you refuse to answer the question, the jury may assume you are guilty.

James

I must still refuse.

Coroner

Is it true that the cry of "Cooee" was a signal between you and your father?

James

Yes.

Coroner

Then why did your father say it before he saw you or knew that you had returned home?

James

I do not know.

Coroner

Did you see anything suspicious when you went back and found your father dying?

James

I saw something lying on the ground to my left as I ran to my father. I think it was a gray cloak. But when I rose from my father's side, it was gone.

Coroner

How far from the body was it?

James

About a dozen yards.

Coroner

How far from the edge of the woods was it?

James

Only a few yards.

Coroner

Could it have been taken away while you were a dozen yards from it?

James

Yes. My back was to it.

Coroner

Thank you. That will be all.

SCENE 5

Back to Holmes and Watson on the train. Watson has finished reading James McCarthy's statements to the coroner. He hands the newspaper back to Holmes.

Watson

There are at least three things wrong with James's story. First, his father signaled to him before he knew that James was nearby. That doesn't make sense. Second, James refused to describe the quarrel with his father. That means he has something to hide. Third, he gave an odd account of his father's last words. He must have made up that business about "a rat."

Holmes

(Smiling) I'd say those last two points make James seem innocent. It would take quite an imagination to make up that account of his father's last words. But if James had such an imagination, he surely could have made up a good reason for the quarrel with his father.

SCENE 6

An inn in Boscombe Valley. Holmes and Watson are eating lunch. Detective Lestrade is with them, explaining why Holmes was called in on the case.

Lestrade

It is clear that James McCarthy is guilty. But Miss Alice Turner had heard of you and wanted to know your opinion. I told her there was nothing you could do which I had not already done. Why, here she is now!

(Alice Turner enters the dining room.)

Alice

(Excitedly) I'm so glad you are here, Mr. Holmes. I know that James did not commit this terrible crime. He and I have known each other since we were little children. He would not hurt a fly.

Holmes

I hope we can clear him, Miss Turner.

Alice

Do you think he is innocent then?

Holmes

I think that is very likely.

Alice

(To Lestrade) You see?

Lestrade

I think Mr. Holmes has formed an opinion too quickly.

Alice

No. He is right. James is not guilty. You may wonder why he refused to describe the quarrel with his father. I am sure that the quarrel was about me.

Holmes

Why?

Alice

Mr. McCarthy wanted James to marry me. James and I are very close, but James is young. He does not want to get married yet. So there were quarrels, and I am sure this was one of them.

Holmes

What does *your* father think of such a marriage?

Alice

He is against it.

Holmes

May I see your father if I go to your house tomorrow?

Alice

The doctor will not allow it. My father has not been well for many years. And now, Mr. McCarthy's murder has broken him down completely. Mr. McCarthy was the only person around here who knew my father in the old days in Australia.

Holmes

Isn't that where your father made his money?

Alice

Yes. A gold mine made him rich.

Holmes

Thank you, Miss Turner. You have been very helpful.

Alice

I must go home now and take care of my father. When you see James, tell him I know he is innocent.

Holmes

I will.

Alice

Good-bye. *(She leaves.)*

Lestrade

Holmes, you have raised her hopes. I call that cruel.

Holmes

No. I think I know how to clear James McCarthy. I will visit him in jail this afternoon.

SCENE 7

A cell in the jail. Holmes has just finished questioning James McCarthy.

Holmes

Miss Turner wanted me to tell you that she is sure you are innocent.

James

Dear Alice. I don't deserve her faith in me.

Holmes

What do you mean?

James

Mr. Holmes, I am very much in love with Alice. But I did a crazy thing two years ago, before I fell in love with her. She had been away at a boarding school for five years. I was very lonely, and I married a waitress I hardly knew. I told no one about this. When my father tried to get me to marry Alice, I wanted to, but I could not. Do you recall that I was away for three days just before my father's death?

Holmes

Yes.

James

I was trying to get a divorce from my wife. She lives in Bristol.

Holmes

Your father didn't know where you were, did he?

James

No.

Holmes

Was your wife willing to get divorced?

James

Not at first. But when she learned that I've been arrested for murder, she sent me this letter. *(He shows a letter to Holmes.)* She admits that she was already married when we met. So our marriage is not legal. Naturally I am relieved.

SCENE 8

The next morning, Holmes, Watson, and Lestrade are walking to the scene of the crime.

Lestrade

Mr. Turner had a bad night. The doctor says he does not have long to live. McCarthy's death has obviously upset him a good deal. McCarthy was an old friend of his, and Turner helped him in many ways. He even let McCarthy live on part of his farm without paying any rent.

Holmes

I'd think that McCarthy would feel he owed Turner quite a lot. So I find it strange that he assumed that his son could marry Alice without even asking her. It is even

46

stranger since we know that Turner didn't want them to get married. Alice told us so.

Lestrade

You can raise all the questions you want, Holmes. I know that McCarthy was killed by his son. *(He stops walking and points at the ground.)* There is the spot where the body was found.

Watson

You can still see where McCarthy fell, because the ground is still damp.

Holmes

I measured the boots of both father and son on the way here. *(He points.)* Those are James's footprints. First he walked here and away. Then he ran here and away. Where he ran, the prints are deeper and farther apart. This fits in with his story. He ran when he heard his father cry out and right after his father died.

Lestrade

Those footprints look pretty much the same to me.

(Holmes is now examining the ground under a tree at the edge of the woods. He picks up a rock.)

Holmes

This may interest you, Lestrade. The murder was done with this.

Lestrade

What makes you think so?

Holmes

Grass is growing under it. That means it has been resting here only a few days.

Lestrade

(Sarcastically) I suppose you can describe the murderer for me.

Holmes

Yes. He is tall and left-handed. He limps with his right leg. He sometimes wears thick-soled boots and a gray cloak. He smokes cigars, uses a cigar-holder, and carries a blunt knife in his pocket.

Lestrade

(Laughing) I am afraid you will find it hard to convince a jury of all that.

Holmes
(Turning to Watson) We have a small job to do this afternoon. Then we shall probably go back to London by the evening train.

Lestrade
But aren't you going to finish your case?

Holmes
It is finished. The mystery is solved.

Lestrade
Then who is the criminal?

Holmes
I have just described him. It shouldn't be hard to find him in a small village like this.

SCENE 9

Holmes and Watson are back at the inn. They are having lunch in their sitting room.

Watson
Holmes, I am confused about two details. Why would McCarthy cry "Cooee" before he knew his son was around? And why would he refer to "a rat" as he died?

Holmes
The cry of "Cooee" was not mean for his son. It was meant for the person he had an appointment with. "Cooee" is an Australian cry. So McCarthy probably expected to meet an Australian at Boscombe Pond.

Watson
What about the rat then?

Holmes

(Unfolding a map) This is a map of Australia. *(He points to a place on it.)* What do you read there?

Watson

"Ballarat."

Holmes

Right. That was what the dying man said. His son heard only the last part of it—*arat*. The father was trying to name his murderer—so-and-so, of Ballarat.

Watson

I see.

Holmes

James told us about a gray cloak. I think the murderer was an Australian from Ballarat with a gray cloak.

Watson

Of course! *(Pause)* But how could you describe him in so much detail to Lestrade? I know you could judge his height from the length of his stride. You could tell the kind of boots he wore from his footprints. But how could you tell me he is lame?

Holmes

The mark of his right foot was always lighter than his left. He put less weight on it because he was lame.

Watson

How could you tell he is left-handed?

Holmes

McCarthy's death blow was on the left side of the back of his head. So the blow was probably delivered by a left-handed man.

Watson

What about the cigars and the cigar-holder?

Holmes

This man stood behind a tree while McCarthy and his son quarreled. Next to the tree I found the butt of a cigar. I could tell that it had not been in his mouth. Therefore, he had used a holder. The tip of the cigar had been cut off, but not sharply. So I concluded that he had used a blunt knife.

Watson

Holmes, you have drawn a net around the real murderer. And you have saved the life of an innocent man.

(There is a knock on the door. Holmes opens it, and John Turner limps into the room. He is a tall man, and he looks very ill.)

Holmes

Good afternoon, Mr. Turner. Did you get my note?

Turner

(Sitting down) Yes.

Holmes

I know all about McCarthy's past and yours.

Turner

(Sadly) I thought so. But I want you to know that I would not have let James come to harm! I was going to tell the truth if it went against him in court.

Holmes

I'm glad to hear you say so.

Turner

I would have spoken up sooner if it weren't for my daughter. It would break her heart if I were arrested. I'm a dying man, Mr. Holmes. The doctor says I'll be dead within a month. For my daughter's sake, I must not die in jail.

Holmes

I am not a police officer, Mr. Turner. Your daughter hired me to look into this case. My job is to act in her interests. James McCarthy must be freed, though.

Turner

What should I do?

Holmes

(Picking up a pen and some paper) Just tell us the truth, I will write it down. Then you will sign it, and Watson can witness it. I will use it only if I have to.

Turner

Very well. *(Pause)* Years ago, I went digging for gold in Australia, but I had no luck. I joined some highway robbers called the Ballarat Gang, and I became known as Black Jack of Ballarat. One day, we held up a wagon carrying gold from one of the mines. The driver was Charles McCarthy, and I wish I had not spared his life. *(He starts coughing.)*

Watson

Why did you hate McCarthy so much?

Turner

You will see in a moment. The Ballarat Gang fled to England with the gold. Then I quit the gang and settled down to a respectable life. I married a woman who died young, but she left me my dear Alice.

Watson

She is a lovely young woman. You should be proud of her.

Turner

Oh, I am. Because of Alice, I tried to do good things with my money—to make up for my past. All went well until Charles McCarthy showed up.

Watson

I see. Did he threaten to tell the police about your past?

Turner

Yes—unless I gave him whatever he asked for. So I gave him land, money, a house. But finally he asked for the one thing I could not give. He asked for Alice. He knew I was in poor health, and he wanted James to marry Alice in order to get my property. We planned to met at Boscombe Pond to try to settle the matter.

Holmes

When you got there, did you hear McCarthy and his son quarreling?

Turner

Yes. I waited behind a tree until James left. As I listened, I became furious. It drove me mad to think that what I held most dear might come under the power of that devil. So I struck him. I know that I have sinned but I have also suffered. And I could not let my daughter suffer, too.

Watson

What happened after you hit McCarthy?

Turner

He cried out. James heard him and ran back. I hid behind a tree, but I had to go back to get the cloak I had dropped. That is what happened, gentlemen. I swear that it is true.

Holmes

(Handing his pen to Turner) Well , it is not for me to judge you.

Turner

(Signing the confession) What will you do with this?

Holmes

If James McCarthy is found guilty, I will have to use it to clear him. Otherwise, I will do nothing. You have already been sentenced to die soon. And when you die, you will have to answer for your deeds.

Turner

Farewell, then. And thank you.

SCENE 10

Several months later in London, Holmes and Watson are having lunch together.

Holmes

There is an announcement in today's paper that Alice Turner and James McCarthy were married.

Watson

That's nice. It's a good thing that James was found innocent so that John Turner's secret could be kept from Alice.

Holmes

When Turner died, I believe his secret died with him. It seems likely that Alice and James will never have to be haunted by their father's deeds.

This book was set in Cheltenham
and composed by Marjorie Campolongo.
It was printed on 50 lb. Finch Opaque.
Title page illustration by Eva Vagretti Cockrille

Editor: Deborah Jerome-Cohen
Design: Patricia Isaza